Goats for Beginners

by

Maggi Franklin

**Edited by Sara Roadnight
and Michael Roberts**

Illustrated by Sara Roadnight

Cover photograph: Tambo Herd of Saanen and British Saanen goats

Published by Gold Cockerel Books 2005

ISBN 9780 947870 478

The Author

There can be few people better qualified to write about practical goat keeping than Maggi Franklin who started keeping goats in 1972. The 1970s were popular years for goatkeeping with self-sufficiency very much on the agenda after the 1960s, and many of today's more experienced breeders started out at around the same time. It was within this environment of optimism that Maggi's love of the Anglo-Nubian breed was to take root and flourish after her purchase of Wayward Antonia, the founder member of the now world famous Tyegronon Herd.

Much has been achieved by this small herd which has specialised exclusively in ANs - not the easiest breed within which to achieve consistent results in the show ring. The Tyegronon ANs, known for their trademark colouration, have been at the top of the tree ever since, producing Champions and Breed Champions as well as the highest milk recorded AN ever. Only three AN herds have bred dam and daughter full Champions in the history of the breed, the Tyegronon herd being one of them.

I first met Maggi in 1973, when I went to inspect a set of quadruplets for export; they duly went abroad and Tyegronon goats have subsequently been much sought after in countries around the world. The home market has not been neglected either, with many AN herds benefiting from infusions of Tyegronon blood, as either foundation females or stud males, and the herd has had a major influence on the AN breed development over the years.

Maggi has also been generous with her time, advising novice goat keepers, supporting local clubs and serving on the BGS committee as well as appearing regularly in the show ring. In addition, she is a popular BGS licensed judge, officiating at shows up and down the country. All this has been fitted in around a busy home life with husband Harry and daughter Gabrielle.

The skilled breeding policy, in-depth knowledge, excellent management skills and practical common sense all combine to make Maggi Franklin the ideal author of this book.

Andrew Morrey.

Acknowledgements

I would like to thank Michael Roberts and Sara Roadnight who have made this book possible; all those who have allowed me to use photographs of their goats; Virginia Crane and Angela Winterton for their support and time, and the latter for her talent with a camera; Andrew Morrey for his kind words; my daughter Gabrielle and her camera skills which have also played their part; The British Goat Society which I have mentioned on a number of occasions throughout Goats for Beginners; and finally my own goats, the Tyegronon Anglo Nubians, who have given me such pleasure and taught me so much.

Maggi Franklin
September 2005

CONTENTS

ERRATA

Page 29
For Low hocks read cow hocked

Page 32
For biannually read biennially

Goats for Beginners.

A return to the good life and self sufficiency may well spring to mind at the thought of keeping goats, with lots of healthy fresh milk and cheese as part of an idyllic rural life style. This could well be the case, but it will also mean responsibility and hard work such as mucking out on cold, wet winter days. Tending your animals will involve a lot more than just milking them twice a day, 365 days a year.

If you are really keen to keep goats and are not put off by the idea of hard work and responsibility, then the next step is to consider how many to start with. I very strongly recommend having at least two, as goats are gregarious creatures and need companionship. It must be stressed that however lovable and tame they are, goats are livestock and should be treated accordingly.

It is possible to keep goats in a back garden but they will have to be stall fed; this means that you will be the provider and must be prepared to cut and carry everything to them. You will have to think about exercising your animals and consider any impact on your neighbours. You will also need to plan a regular and efficient cleaning routine; muck heaps should not be allowed to grow too big or spread too wide. All these factors will apply whichever way you decide to keep your goats. Obviously the more land you have at your disposal the better. A well fenced paddock with a warm dry shelter would be ideal; failing this, perhaps a yard with a goat house attached.

Goat Facts

Contrary to popular belief goats do not eat just anything but can be very choosy. They may however, sometimes try things which are not good for them, (see Poisonous plants, page 61). They are also very wasteful, food dropped on the floor might as well be thrown away. Food and water containers must be kept scrupulously clean. Use plain water for this as aromas left from cleaning liquids could well stop the goat from eating or drinking out of its clean bowl, a good example of how fussy they can be!

Goats are herd animals and should not be kept on their own.

Goats are very intelligent and soon learn their names like dogs.

Goats hate getting wet so it is essential that they have access to shelter at all times.

Goats are browsers and tethering is not a good option.

Goats do not make good lawn mowers as they will only eat what they choose. Lush orchard grass is not always a goat's idea of heaven but the fruit trees may well be! Goats prefer fibrous food.

Goats are by nature inquisitive and will nibble and investigate most things out of curiosity, even the washing on the line if they get the chance, although they are very selective about what they eat.

Uncastrated male goats have a very strong, distinctive odour, especially during the mating season. Female goats kept in good condition should smell of nothing other than sweet hay and clean bedding. A healthy goat's droppings are dry which means they are much easier animals to keep clean than cows.

Goat's milk can sometimes have a taint. If the animals are kept clean and the milk is hygienically produced it should taste little different from cow's milk, perhaps slightly sweeter. A strong or 'goaty' taste means that the milk has probably not been produced correctly or the goat has been fed with too much of a particular food, e.g. brassicas

Both male and female goats grow beards.

It is advisable not to play with your goats, particularly young kids. If a small kid pushes against you, never push it back, just walk away. What seems like a game when the goat is small could develop into a very nasty habit as it grows up. Goats will butt each other, which is quite natural; it is their way of developing an order of herd dominance.

The main difference between goats and sheep is their coats: goats have hair, sheep have wool.

Questions to ask yourself if you want dairy goats:

Are you prepared to milk them twice a day 365 days a year?

What about holidays? Who will tend your goats if you are away?

If you should be taken ill is there someone responsible who could look after your goats?

Read the section on tethering; could you cope with this?

Are you able to dispose of all the soiled bedding?

Can you tell the difference between good and bad hay? Goats will only eat the very best quality hay.

Restraining your goat

It is not a good idea to leave collars on goats when they are unattended; it is natural for these animals to climb and they could very easily get caught by their collars and hang themselves. Never leave collars on kids. When leading a goat keep the collar high up the neck and walk beside the animal. The windpipe and jugular vein can become compressed if the animal pulls, causing it to drop to the ground and choke. If this happens release the pressure immediately and rub the area. Headcollars can be used on goats, but again, these should never be left on when the animals are unsupervised.

Tethering

This is the worst method of controlling goats and is seldom done correctly. If it is really the only option then it must be carried out correctly.

Make sure that you buy a tether with two swivels, one at the collar end and one at the peg end. The chain must be as light as possible and not less than 3.5 metres long.

Begin tether training in a confined space such as the goat's pen, making sure there are no other animals in there at the time. Tether the goat on a fairly short rope and keep an eye on it while it is tied up; do not leave it unattended. Carry out this procedure for a short while daily, gradually lengthening the rope while keeping the goat in its pen. When you are sure the animal has become accustomed to being restrained you can try tethering it outside. Attach the tether line to the collar and walk the goat out to the full extent of the rope. Never leave it unattended to begin with. Goats tethered during the day should always be free in their pens at night.

A tethered goat should be moved at least twice a day to a fresh patch; they will never eat from ground that they have soiled. Water must be available all the time. If you tether on a bank always put the peg at the bottom of the slope, never at the top or halfway down: a goat can hang itself on its rope. If there is no shelter from the elements you must be ready to bring your goat in if the weather gets very hot or wet, and always remember to bring in any tethered animals if you are going out; it's not safe to leave a tethered goat completely unattended. Never tether two or more animals close together, and don't tether them if there is a chance they will be browsing as they could easily get tangled up. Kids should NEVER be tethered.

All things considered, electric fencing is a far better solution!

Palatable plant - Hazel

BASIC NEEDS

Housing
Goats should have access to adequate shelter at all times. They can suffer acutely in prolonged rain or very hot sunshine, and they hate the flies in summer. They have very little oil in their coats, unlike sheep, and if left out in the rain can soon become soaked to the skin and could run the risk of developing pneumonia or some other disease.

Feeding
Providing it has access to fresh clean pasture and browsings, a goat that is non-productive can look after itself without discomfort from May through to August, with hay at night in the shelter and on wet days. If grazing is in short supply, especially during the winter, then a concentrate maintenance ration should be fed as well as palatable hay ad lib. All productive (milking, fibre and meat) goats must have a concentrate ration and those that are dry but in kid will require a concentrate feed for the last two months of pregnancy, (see the chapter on feeding, page 48).

Milking
A dairy goat in milk should either suckle kids or be milked twice a day after kidding.

Feet
The goats' feet will need to be trimmed regularly, about every 6 to 8 weeks.

Medication
Goats require regular medication against internal parasites, and a suitable pour-on should be applied to prevent or eradicate lice. Don't forget to note the milk withdrawal time if milk is being used for human consumption. If a goat is sick or injured the law requires that it should be given skilled attention.

Unwanted animals

If a goat is no longer wanted and there is no caring, responsible person willing to take it, or if it is old or ailing, it should be humanely destroyed by either a licensed slaughter man or a veterinary surgeon. Contact DEFRA for up to date information on the subject.

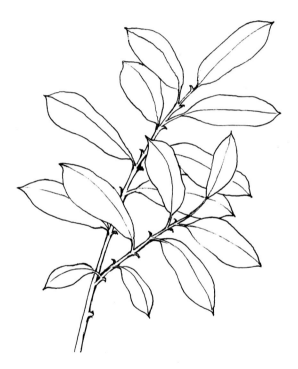

Palatable plant - Goat Willow

WHERE TO BEGIN

Everyone keeping farm animals is required by law to register their stock and holding with the Department for Environment, Food and Rural Affairs, and this includes people wishing to keep goats. You will be given a holding number, and a herd mark number which will be used on stock bred on your holding. It is illegal to keep goats that are not identifiable by ear tags. Stock born from July 2005 must carry ear tags. DEFRA will supply you with the appropriate forms which will need completing when moving stock on or off your holding.

Learn to milk before you buy your goats. It's not usually a good idea to buy animals from your local newspaper. The British Goat Society (see Useful Addresses at the back of the book) will be able to put you in touch with local breeders and affiliated goat societies throughout the United Kingdom. Several societies have their own websites which provide information about the different breeds, and a County Show is the ideal place to visit if you want to see a good variety of goats together.

When you come to buy a goat try to choose one with the highest possible health status (see page 32). People often ask which is the best dairy breed, and the answer is, there isn't one; there are good and bad milkers to be found in all breeds. Go for the type of goat which pleases your eye the most. After all, you will be looking after it for 365 days of the year.

DIFFERENT BREEDS OF GOAT AND THEIR USES

Dairy breeds

In 1919 the United Kingdom had just two recognised distinct breeds of dairy goat, the Toggenburg and Anglo-Nubian which accounted for 20% of B.G.S. Herd Book registrations. The remainder were Anglo-Nubian Swiss goats where the best strains from each breed and from any small importations had been intermingled.

Today there are now eight different breeds of dairy goat. As well as these the B.G.S. recognises cross breeding and has sections in its herd book for such animals to be registered so goats can upgrade to breed sections; so it is now possible for cross-bred goats to upgrade eventually to either Anglo-Nubian, British Alpine, British Saanen, British Toggenburg or British Guernsey. The exceptions are Pure Saanen, Pure Toggenburg and the Golden Guernsey: all have their own closed herd books. The British Alpine, British Toggenburg and Toggenburg all have white markings round the tail and on the legs, face and ears. These are referred to as "Swiss markings". It's important to remember that any goats which are cross bred or grading up may also have these markings. Goats being graded up to a specific herd book section are referred to as Any Other Variety (A.O.V.). These goats can sometimes show mis-markings.

Anglo-Nubian

This breed has its ancestral roots in the Middle East. At the end of the nineteenth and beginning of the twentieth centuries these goats were taken on board P & O steamers to provide the passengers with a supply of fresh milk. Once the ships docked in London these goats were eagerly bought by interested goat keepers who bred them with indigenous goats in the U.K. The resulting cross breeds gained the name Anglo-Nubian. During this period four male goats of Eastern type, originating from India and the Middle East, were brought to England. These males were very important in the history of the breed.

The Anglo-Nubian is very popular, its two most distinguishing features being its markedly convex "Roman" nose and long pendulous ears. The stance is upright and the demeanour proud and supercilious; the coat can be a variety of attractive colours or mixtures. No neck tassels are allowed. The Anglo-Nubian's voice differs from that of other breeds, rather in the same way as a Siamese cat's voice differs from that of an 'ordinary' cat. The Anglo-Nubian's milk is high in butterfat and protein in comparison with other dairy breeds; this helps to develop cheese yield and is excellent for yogurt and butter making.

Anglo-Nubians are very prolific breeders: twins are the norm, triplets are not rare and quadruplets and even quins occur quite frequently. The Anglo-Nubian is the largest of the dairy breeds.

13

British Alpine

This breed was developed in Britain although goats of this type could be found in France and Switzerland before the turn of the twentieth century. It is generally acknowledged that the starting point for the breed in the U.K. was the importation of Sedgemere Faith from France in 1903. The British Alpine is a large rangy goat, very smart with a black coat and white "Swiss markings". The facial line can be dished (concave) or straight, and these goats can appear with or without neck tassels.

British Saanen

As the British Saanen is founded on the pure Saanen imported into the U.K. from Switzerland in the early 1900s it is obviously of more recent origin. After a further importation of Saanens in 1922 rapid progress was made and in 1925 the B.G.S. opened their section in the Herd Book. To the uninitiated most white goats appear to be Saanens, but they are more likely to be either British Saanens or upgrades. In general this breed has a calm temperament; the facial line is straight or slightly dished and the animals can be with or without neck tassels. The coat hair is white although the skin can have patches of black.

British Toggenburg

This is another breed that was developed in Britain, founded upon imported Toggenburgs and pedigree cross bred goats of Swiss origin. The B.G.S. opened a section for them in 1925. The coat colour varies from dark to light brown, although mid brown is generally preferred, with white "Swiss Markings". These goats can be with or without neck tassels.

The Saanen

This all white goat originates in Switzerland and has a most agreeable placid temperament. The Saanen blood lines in Britain are mainly founded upon imported goats from Switzerland with a little new blood from the Dutch White goat. Neck tassels are allowed.

14

The Toggenburg

This is another Swiss breed. The coat can range in colour from silver fawn to mid brown with white "Swiss Markings". The hair can be any length, often growing in fringes on flanks and quarters, and the goat can be with or without neck tassels.

Golden Guernsey

As its name suggests, this goat originated in Guernsey and the first animals came to mainland Britain in 1965. A distinctive feature is the colour of the coat which ranges from pale blond to deep bronze. Some animals have small white markings and a blaze or star on their heads, but neck tassels and "Swiss Markings" are not allowed. The coat hair can be long or short.

British Guernsey

In 1973 the B.G.S. started a scheme which allowed Saanen or British Saanen males to be used on Golden Guernsey females, grading up from that first cross being via Golden Guernsey males. The British Guernsey has the same characteristics as the Golden Guernsey but is often slightly larger. Neck tassels are allowed.

The English

Prior to the twentieth century this was the most common goat in the British Isles, but when foreign goats began to be imported the pure blood lines started to become diluted. However, the English blood lines and characteristics have survived to the extent that it is still possible to breed selectively for English characteristics. The coat is fairly short and dense but long fringes on the back and flanks and thicker tufts on the legs are allowed. The colours are various shades of brown or grey with a dark eel line or stripe along the back, and down the neck, legs and flanks. Neck tassels are naturally absent.

PRIMARILY FIBRE BREEDS

The Angora

This is one of the oldest recorded breeds of goat and is mentioned in the Bible (Exodus, chapter 35 verse 26). It is kept for its coat, the luxury fibre mohair which the textile industry calls "the diamond fibre" as it is so hard wearing and has a beautiful lustre to it.

Angoras are generally smaller than the dairy breeds and need shearing twice a year. Breeders who show would expect to shear the goats as soon as possible after January 1st and kid early in February or early March. The second shearing takes place in late August just prior to mating at the beginning of September. For those who do not wish to show, shearing times can vary but must take place twice a year as the coat grows fast at an inch per month. As the goat grows older the hair becomes coarser: the best quality therefore comes from young kids. It is important to feed Angoras well as they require protein to produce consistently top quality mohair.

The Cashmere

As yet there is no single recognised breed of cashmere goat in the U.K. Cashmere is the name of the fine undercoat or down which can be present in most dairy breeds, but the quantity produced is very small and the length of fibre too short for it to have any commercial value. The feral goats found in parts of the British Isles can be regarded as native cashmere-producing goats. They carry significant amounts of cashmere which is as good as any found elsewhere in the world.

A PRIMARILY MEAT BREED

The Boer

This breed originated in South Africa, the first studs being established in Britain in 1988; the Boer found its way to this country via Ireland, Israel, France and West Germany. It has a very distinctive colouring with a white body and chestnut brown head. Its size and conformation make it an excellent breed for meat production.

PRIMARILY NON-PRODUCTIVE BREEDS

The Bagot

It is believed that a herd of Bagot goats was presented to Sir John Bagot by Richard II. Documentary evidence of the continuous existence of a herd of goats in Bagot's Park (close to Abbots Bromley, Staffordshire) is sparse however. The colour of their coats, black heads and forequarters and the rest white, is very similar to that of the Schwarzhal goats in Switzerland. There is a theory that Bagot goats are descendants of animals brought back from Europe, perhaps by the Crusaders. There are a number of other suggestions as well but none that can be clearly substantiated.

Bagots are small to medium in size with large curving horns. Their coat hair is long and many animals now show spots and patches of black on their hind quarters and small white face blazes. These are permitted but are considered to be faults that will be bred out if numbers increase enough to allow for improvement. Bagot goats are on the Rare Breeds Survival Trust Register.

The Pygmy

These goats originated in Africa and are genetically small, cobby and compact. The head and neck are short and the legs sturdy and short in relation to body length. All colours and markings are acceptable except pure white, and no white "Swiss Markings" are allowed on the face. The breed is genetically horned but disbudding is permitted, which the author would always recommend.

GENETIC FAULTS TO BE FOUND IN ALL BREEDS

The following genetic faults are not acceptable in any dairy breeds:

Mouth or jaw, over-shot, under-shot or twisted.

Testicals, not properly descended or less than two.

Teat defects of any kind, super numerary, fish-tail (divided teat), multiple orifices, etc.

17

WAYS TO KEEP GOATS

With land for grazing and a suitable goat house

The fences must be secure but make sure you never use barbed wire. A good dense hedge is fine, just don't forget your goats will prune it! If you have post and rail fences make sure the lower rails are close enough together to stop kids getting out; they are very clever at squeezing through the smallest of gaps. The top rail of the fence should be about 44" or 112cms high. Pig wire is suitable for your fencing but will require a wooden top rail and ideally another at ground level. A disadvantage is that goats can sometimes get their heads stuck in the wire. Electric fencing is excellent although never completely goat proof, but then very little fencing is! Goats that continually escape from their paddock are usually trying to tell you something: they could be hungry or the paddock may be goat sick. If a hedge separates the enclosure from the garden, please remember that a lot of cultivated hedging is poisonous (see section on poisonous plants.)

Keeping Goats in a Yard

This will require good permanent fencing and a concrete floor. Access to a shelter is essential.

The Goat House

The size of the goat house will depend on the number of goats you keep. It must be light and airy and free from draughts. Windows must be high up and safe. Door catches must be out of reach as goats are clever at undoing some bolts and fastenings and can sometimes get their mouths caught while they are doing this. Each stall must have a hay rack, never use nets. (See the diagram for a no-waste hay rack, page 48.) Food and water buckets are best attached to the outside of the stall with holes for the goat to put its head through for eating and drinking. Having these on the outside means the food and water stay fresh and clean, and the goat will not be able to stand in the buckets and foul the water or tip it into its bed. Remember, food stood on by the goat will end up wasted.

A dry area in which to store hay and straw and a vermin proof container for dry feed will be needed. A large dustbin is ideal for this.

When you decide that you are properly equipped to provide for your goats you can then think about what breed will suit you best.

Entire male goats are not a good idea, and even if you plan to breed from your females at some stage in the future, you do not need to keep a male goat. Goat keepers will stand male goats at stud, and providing your animal is of the correct health status, fit and well, they are usually willing to have visiting female goats. Artificial insemination (AI) is another option available these days.

If you want to keep goats as pets then either gender will suffice but the males need to be castrated by a vet; never keep an entire male goat as a pet. Avoid goats with horns; they can cause damage not only to you but to each other, not to mention their housing. Although pygmy goats are small they can still inflict a lot of damage if they have horns, and it's not a good idea to keep horned pygmys if you have small children about the place.

Kids

These are young goats up to the age of 12 months. Never buy kids less than one month old. A kid will be very unhappy without company of its own kind so it is best to get two. Most dairy breeds are disbudded, (horn buds stopped from growing) when very young, at about a week old. Kids will need milk for the first four months of their lives, and must have a dry, well ventilated but draught free house to shelter them from the elements. If they are unwell they will need veterinary treatment quickly.

With this age group you will obviously have much longer to wait for your milk supply if you are keen to have milk for the house. Goats are normally put in kid for the first time when they are approximately 18 months old and have become goatlings.

Goatlings and buckings

Goatlings are young females between the ages of one and two. They usually become milkers in their second year. Some goatlings can come into milk

19

without being mated and are then referred to as 'maiden milkers'. Buckings are young males in the same age group.

Milking goats (milkers) or adult females or males

These are goats usually over the age of two. With this age group you have an instant milk supply once the female goat has kidded.

The dictionary uses the term Nanny goat for an adult female and Billy goat for an adult male; however, most breeders will not use these names, preferring the ones listed above. With some breeds, Angoras for example, the females are known as 'does' and the males as 'bucks'. A castrated male goat (or sheep) is called a 'wether'.

Points to check

Always buy from a reputable breeder, learn to milk before you buy a milker, and make sure you have a reliable supply of goat's milk if you are starting with kids.

Palatable plant - Hawthorn.

WHAT TO LOOK FOR WHEN BUYING A GOAT

It's a good idea to take an experienced goat keeper with you when going to buy your first goats, and it's worth waiting for the right animals so don't be afraid to say no when choosing. Remember also that breed standards must be taken into account if you are buying pedigree animals. The B.G.S. has produced a booklet which covers all U.K. breeds of goat.

If you are buying a milker the following points need to be applied:

The animal should be healthy with no discharge from nose, eyes or under the tail, and her eyes should be bright and kindly.

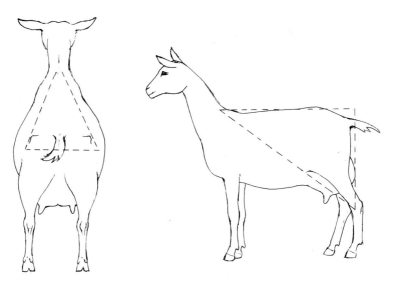

The Dairy Wedge   *The Dairy Wedge from the side*

Stand back and study her, looking from the head to the tail sideways on. The top line should be level with just a little slope to the tail. She should have a slim neck, not thick and bullish, which runs smoothly into the shoulder (withers) with no coarseness. The shoulders must not be too heavy or loose. A milker should be wedge shaped, getting progressively deeper from shoulder

21

to rump, (see drawing page 21) She should have a good spring of rib (not be slab sided) with a generous width of chest between the front legs, all indicating a good bulk eater with a well filled body. She should stand firmly on her feet, which you need to inspect to make sure they have been properly trimmed. Watch her standing and walking on hard ground and check that there is no lameness when she moves; she should not rock back on her heels. Her hind legs from the rear should be straight and fairly wide apart, not cow hocked. It is most important that a goat's feet and legs are sound as they will carry a considerable weight when she is heavily in kid.

A good strong frame is necessary to support the udder, although the udder does not necessarily have to be large to produce a good milk supply. Ideally it should be well attached, both at the front where it runs into the belly, and at the rear, being firmly fixed high up under the hind legs in the escutcheon. The bag should be flat across the bottom and rounded at the back. There is sometimes a cavity or pocket at the front where it joins the belly, but this can be considered undesirable. Teats should be neat and a reasonable shape and size; if they stick out sideways or are long and pendulous, they could be awkward when you are milking. A poor udder, badly attached will swing from side to side, and teats that are too long could be vulnerable to injury or other problems as well.

Feel the udder when it is empty if possible; it should be soft to handle and free of lumps. It is important that you see the goat being milked or ask to milk her yourself. A slow milker with small teat orifices can be a nuisance for a novice.

All in all the goat should be strong and well balanced with a healthy bloom to her coat. Unhealthy goats are generally lethargic with dull coats coarse to the touch. A thin goat is not necessarily an unhealthy one if she is a bright and lively animal. She could well be 'milking off her back'. This means that she is putting all her energy into the milk bucket and keeping nothing for herself, so she would require careful management.

If you decide to start with young stock, either goatlings or kids, look for a lively disposition, length and depth in the body and good bone. Check the teats for possible defects (see page29) and look at the head, both from above between the ears and from the front; the nose must be straight, the jaws should not be over- or under-shot, and the lips should meet together properly. If you are buying a youngster, try to see the dam and check that she has the qualities of a good milker. If she has, you could be heading in the right direction!

Goats, like sheep and cows, never grow front teeth in the top jaw. They have a hard pad which they use in conjunction with their tongue and bottom front teeth when grazing. They have eight milk teeth in the bottom jaw until they are about a year old when the centre pair will drop out to be replaced by a pair of larger permanent incisors. At two and a half years old goats will have four permanent teeth, and usually by the time they are between three and four they will have a complete set and be termed full mouthed. As they age the teeth wear down and eventually fall out. Any animal with four or more permanent teeth who has never kidded should be regarded with caution as she could be a non-breeder.

Useful tip
When buying your goats ask for a small amount of their concentrate feed to tide you over until you can purchase your own. Take care when changing a goat's diet as it is very easy to upset the digestive system.

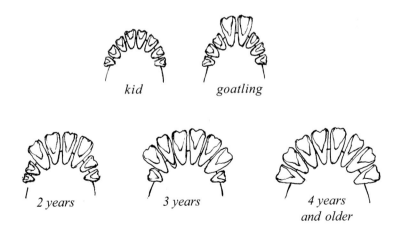

kid   *goatling*

2 years   *3 years*   *4 years and older*

Ageing a goat by its teeth.

Eating from a No Waste Hayrack.

Ready for milking.

24

Surform for shaping goats' feet.

Dairy equipment.

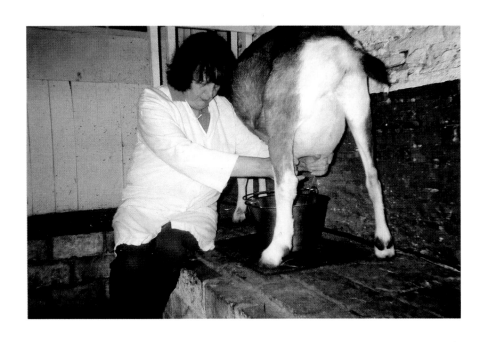

Milking.

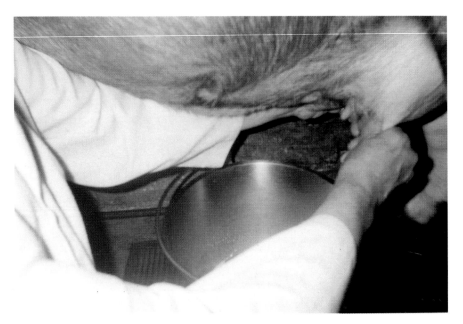

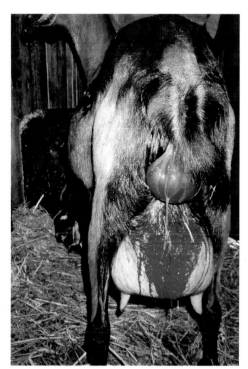

Kidding underway.

Kids all safely arrived.

DAILY ROUTINE

Author's herd: 4 milkers, 2 goatlings, 3 female kids.

7.30 am
Empty and refill all water buckets. Feed concentrate ration. Milk goats then filter and refrigerate the milk. Bottle feed kids. Wash milking equipment and kids' bottles.
Fill hay racks, removing any hay left from overnight. Tidy the pens, sweep the covered yard and corridors and top up the bedding as required.
Let the animals out if the weather permits. Put sugar beet pulp in bucket to soak.

1.30 pm approximately
Bottle feed kids if they are still on 4 milk feeds per day. Bring goats in for beet pulp feed; if the weather is fine they can go outside again after eating.

6.00 pm approximately
Bring the animals in for the night and give the milkers bunches of mixed branches or cut nettles. Bottle feed kids.

7.30 pm
Empty and refill water buckets and feed concentrate ration. Milk, filter and refrigerate as in morning. Wash milking equipment. Top up hay racks and sweep yard and corridors.

10.00 pm
Last bottle of the day for the kids. Give milkers chopped mixed roots or grass supplement. Check hay racks and all animals.

In winter and on wet days when goats are being kept in, hay racks will require topping up throughout the day and the yard may need more frequent sweeping. Milkers will welcome extra branches.

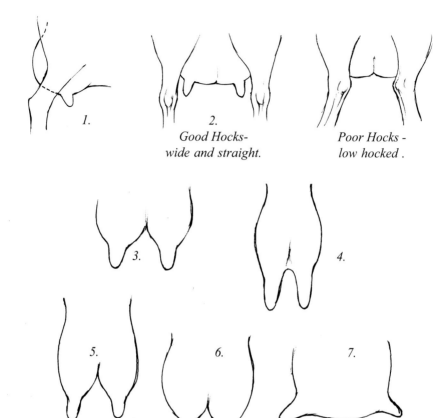

1.

2.
Good Hocks-
wide and straight.

Poor Hocks -
low hocked .

3.   4.   5.   6.   7.

8.   9.   10.   11.

Udder shapes:
1 & 2: Good, well shaped with nice teats correctly placed.
3: Too divided   4: Necky, poor attachment, teats too close and too long.
5: Pendulous udder with badly divided, bottle shaped teats.
6: Very uneven   7: Dropped udder floor.

Teat shapes:
8: Bottle teat   9: Teat too thin   10: No definition between teat and udder.
11: Teat not at base of udder.
Note: Numbers 3 to 11 are all considered undesirable.

WEEKLY ROUTINE

Wash all water and food containers. Clean out all pens and put down fresh, dry, new bedding. If the weather has been good and the animals have spent most of the time outside, you may find that the pens can go for two weeks without cleaning. Kids' pens, however, are best done weekly or even more frequently if you have a lot of animals in the pen, as this will help to avoid infections.

MONTHLY ROUTINE

Foot trimming. Some goats' feet grow quicker than others and this is a job that needs time allocated to it every 4 to 6 weeks. When trimming the feet inspect them for signs of heel mites, foot rot or foreign bodies and treat as appropriate.

January

Routine daily care. Possible last foot trim for goats due to kid. This is best done 4 to 6 weeks before the due date.

February

Routine daily care. Check equipment needed for kidding.

March

Routine daily care. If kidding this month, goats will need careful watching day and night as the kidding date draws near. They usually kid close to the due date.

April

Routine daily care. If kidding this month, keep careful watch day and night as the date draws near. Milkers that have kidded will need foot trimming and worming

May

Routine daily care. When turning your animals out onto grass, start them with a fairly short period of time outside and gradually lengthen it, as too much lush grass can cause digestive problems.

The daily/weekly routine is much the same throughout the spring, summer and autumn. Kids will need their bottle feeds gradually reduced until they are weaned, and you will have to think about any breeding plans you may have for the autumn. Goats are considered to be seasonal breeders but there are exceptions and they can cycle almost any time; however, October to February is the norm.

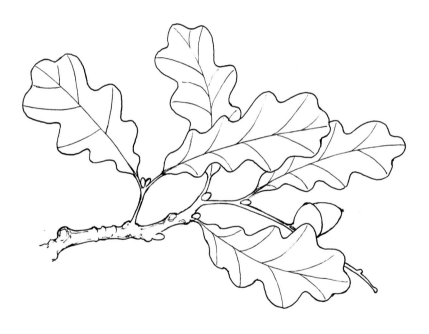

Palatable plant - Oak
(NEVER use oak apples or acorns)
A few oak leaves are fine and very good
for a scouring goat.

HEALTH STATUS

Caprine Arthritis – Encephalitis (CAE)

C.A.E. is a virus disease of goats which can lie dormant for some time before manifesting itself. It must be stressed that this virus is host specific and does not affect humans; as yet there is no cure. In adult goats it causes Arthritis and a form of Mastitis; in young kids it causes Encephalitis and sometimes Pneumonia. It is endemic in many parts of the world, but has been kept under control in this country by dedicated goat breeders, and overseen by the British Goat Society and the Scottish Agricultural College, (S.A.C.). The former oversee dairy goats and a few pygmy goats, and the latter Angoras with a few dairy goats.

C.A.E. Accredited Herd

This is a herd accredited for C.A.E. who are in the S.A.C. health scheme. It is also supported by the B.G.S.

C.A.E. Monitored Herd

This scheme is approved and monitored by the British Goat Society, and is very similar to the S.A.C. scheme. Blood tests are taken biannually.

Private Testing (whole herd)

Here blood testing is carried out annually.

All three of these schemes require blood samples to be taken by a vet, and are aimed at disease (C.A.E.) eradication. The author strongly recommends that when you buy goats they fall into one of these categories. Certificates are given for proof of testing. If buying a kid, you should obtain a certificate of the sire and dam's negative C.A.E. status from the vendor.

Scrapie

DEFRA run a monitored Scrapie scheme for which goats are eligible. Many goat breeders have enrolled in the voluntary scheme but it is compulsory if you are exporting goats to Europe. The Scrapie monitoring scheme needs to be renewed annually. Ask for photocopies of the herd's certificates when you buy your goats, if their herd is in the scheme.

Caseous Lymphadentitis (CL)

At present there are no schemes in place for this chronic disease of sheep and goats. It is highly contagious and is characterised by nodules containing a cheesy pus forming in the lymph nodes, lungs, skin or other organs. If a goat develops a body abscess a very close eye should be kept on it. If in doubt always consult a vet.

Palatable plants - Common Red
and White Clover (white not so popular)

Most stud goat owners are in these health schemes and will only allow their male goats to cover visiting females of equal health status. The herd's health status will be lost if an untested male is used.

BREEDING

It is a widely held belief that mammals must give birth in order to produce milk, but this is not necessarily so in the case of the dairy goat. Some young dairy goats will produce an udder with milk in it when they are only a few months old. It is also not unusual for Swiss type goats to produce milk by the time they are goatlings, but it is best not to encourage this by milking; instead keep a close eye on them and milk them only if the udder becomes tight or hot.

When to mate your goats

Breeding from kids is practiced in some commercial herds but is best left to the experienced breeder.

Goats should be mated for the first time when they are goatlings, thus kidding down at about 2 years of age. Ideally milkers should be mated every other year. Most dairy goats will 'milk through' in the second year, giving approximately half the daily yield of the first year. So in an ideal world if you have two milkers you should have a continuous supply of fresh milk for your household. Arrangements with the stud goat owner should be made in advance, or if an Artificial Inseminator is going to be used make sure they have plenty of time to order the semen required. The normal practice is to contact the stud goat owner/inseminator when your goat has first come in season.

Recognising oestrus or 'heat' or 'season'

This can be a little difficult for those new to goat keeping. You may well be told of various signs that signal the onset of this condition, and in fact there are a number of symptoms of which at least two could be positive.

You will often hear the rhythmic tapping of her tail on the wall of her pen before you see the animal, or you will be greeted by a particular call which may continue after you are no longer in sight. To the novice the tail tapping can be hard to distinguish from the normal quick swish as if troubled by a fly or the 'pleased to see you' wag. Other signs of season are a disinclination to

34

eat and a lot of calling out at the same time, the milk yield may drop, the goat may become fidgety at milking time, she may produce a sticky discharge like egg white which can adhere to the tail, and her vulva may become pink and puffy.

Should you wish to mate the animal but still be unsure if she is ready, you could make a note of the date and watch her; in 21 days, generally the length of time between seasons, she should call again. A season normally lasts approximately 3 days but the first one could last only hours.

If you have decided to have your goat served naturally, make the phone call to the male goat owner and set off as soon as possible. It is usual for the female to be taken to the male, but some stud goat owners will travel to you, in which case travelling expenses would be added to the stud fee. If using AI be advised by the inseminator.

Billy Rag

Most owners of stud male goats will be happy to supply you with a Billy Rag. This is a piece of material impregnated with the odour of a male goat. Keep it in a sealed container and if you are not sure whether your goat is in season, take it out and let her sniff it. If she is in season she will usually respond by wagging her tail.

When you have made the appointment to visit the stud goat and are ready for the journey, you must make sure that you have the correct paperwork with you ie the DEFRA forms and the B.G.S. registration details for your female if she is registered. All this information will be put on the service certificate after mating. Details of movements must also be entered in your stock movement records book.

When you get to your destination you may find your goat has 'gone off'; many goats can temporarily 'go off' with the stress of travelling so you will have to be patient. Don't hurry to introduce her into the male goat's pen but let the animals sniff noses first. Encourage her to eat a little hay and put her into a holding pen, ideally next to the male, for ten minutes, with some good hay; this will often do the trick. The service is not a prolonged affair and is usually over in seconds. Some stud owners will allow a second service before you leave for home. Watch your goat at 5 to 7 days after mating; if she appears to be in season again another visit to the stud goat could well be required.

Should your goat not hold to service she may be given a free second chance three weeks later. When using AI however, you would be expected to pay a second fee.

Care of the in kid goat

Once served, the goat will resume her normal life style. Watch her at 21 days and 42 days to make sure she has not 'turned', that is come into season again.

The gestation period will be from 155 days but kids may be produced successfully any time after 145 days. I use a very simple method to arrive at the due date by counting five months forward and taking away one day, so that if the mating took place on 2nd November you could expect kids around 1st April

Drying off to stop milk production

Once the goat has been sucessfully mated her milk yield should begin to drop. An in kid goat will need two or three months dry at the end of the gestation period in which to build up her reserves for the growing kids and the next lactation. The good food that she has been eating and turning into milk is now needed for the kids she is carrying.

There are various ways to dry off a milker; some goats even do it themselves once past 21 days of pregnancy. Most will drop their yield with just a little encouragement if you start to milk them once a day instead of twice then cut that down to every other day. Some breeders will bite the bullet and just stop milking altogether. After the last milking insert veterinary dry cow treatment tubes into the teats and then keep checking that the udder does not heat up, go red or get too hard. Some very heavy milkers can never be dried off completely; these animals should be well fed and just eased not 'stripped out', that is total removal of all that day's milk.

Don't forget to attend to your pregnant goats' feet; they should be trimmed about four weeks before the due date.

Exercise is most important. Turning your goats out on a cold day into a wet, muddy field is not a good idea, they will just stand and shiver and could easily catch a chill. Encourage them to walk with you, or if space in your goat house allows, leave the pen doors open so they can move around the corridor. A covered yard if you have one, would be excellent for exercise. Always take care not to let your goats get cold.

Kidding

Before kidding make sure you have the following items collected together and kept near where they will be needed:

a) Rolls of kitchen paper for drying off newborn kids, approximately six rolls for one goat who delivers twins. Old towels are useful but not very pleasant to wash after use.

b) Antiseptic spray or iodine solution for treating the kids' navels. Your vet will supply you with something suitable.

c) Dettol or a similar disinfectant for hand washing and a clean bucket or bowl.

d) Lamb teat and bottle for kids.

e) Box for kids (important for multiple births).

f) An infra red heat lamp. Don't forget to check that it works!

g) A goat coat, (see diagram).

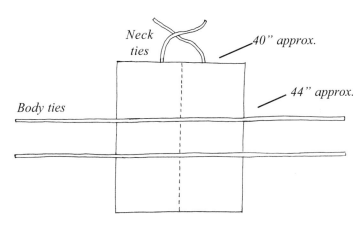

A very simple home-made Goat Rug with long ties which cross under the belly and tie on top of the goat's back.

Make a careful study of your goat's rump so that when kidding time draws near you will be able to recognise that changes are taking place: bones will start to loosen around the tail area and hollows will appear on either side of her tail.

Goatlings usually start to develop udders about six weeks before the due date; the udder of an animal that has previously kidded may not fill so quickly.

Prepare the goat's pen about two weeks before kidding. Scrub it thoroughly with disinfectant (washing soda solution works well) and when everything is dry put down a good bed of straw. If space allows, make an area in one corner for the kid box. If you do this well before the due date the goat will be able to get used to the new arrangements and won't be spooked just when peace and calm are required.

Signs of imminent kidding

Signs that kidding is imminent are numerous. The goat's udder will fill up very quickly, her flanks will hollow and the tail bone will often ridge up or can feel quite slack. She may seem to "talk" to her sides and become restless, or she may not want to go out with the others or eat her feed. She may get quite noisy and bleat whenever she sees you or even call after you when you leave. You could find her pawing her bedding as if trying to make a nest, or lying down and standing up again. You will notice a colourless discharge like egg white coming from the vulva and as she gets closer to kidding she will make a deep grunting bleat every time she strains.

The birth

Over the years I have watched many goats giving birth. All the signs are there and the date is right; just one more grunt, and I wait with bated breath, is this it? ...... no, she begins to cud then chew contentedly. I go and make a cup of tea; things could still take a while. (When you keep goats you begin to see where the saying "who's kidding" comes from!) It may take several more hours but finally she begins to strain with even stronger contractions. The colourless discharge changes to a thicker white and a shiny balloon-like membrane bag appears at the vagina. This should break and if everything is normal you should see two front feet and, a little further back, the kid's nose. Things can take a little time but the goat should be able to cope perfectly well. Often with the next contraction there is a loud wail as the kid's head is pushed through the vulva; once this is achieved

Normal and abnormal presentations

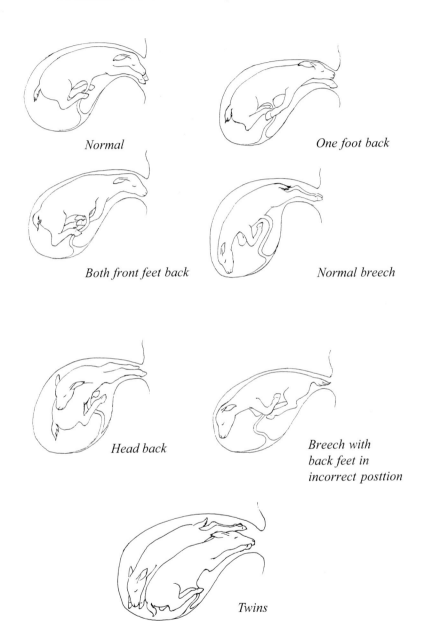

Normal

One foot back

Both front feet back

Normal breech

Head back

Breech with back feet in incorrect posttion

Twins

the rest of its body will follow rapidly. Most goats give birth lying down, but if the mother is standing you must be ready to help lower the kid to the straw. Place it close to the mother's head so she can lick it dry. You can help her with your paper towels, in fact you may be left to complete the drying if she starts producing more kids. Wipe the kid's nose and mouth to remove any mucus, then spray the navel cord to prevent infection getting in; this also helps dry it up. I always put the kids in the corner already prepared (known in our household as the kid cot). The sides are low enough for the mother to be able to lick and nuzzle the kid but high enough to prevent it getting out. Using a kid cot prevents the goat from accidentally standing or rolling on her young which could happen if she starts to produce more kids; first time mothers can be very clumsy.

If there is a second kid it normally follows fairly quickly with very little trouble. Twins are usual and singles are common as are triplets. My goats have had quadruplets on many occasions; one first kidder brought forth four healthy kids in her first year and the next year had five!

If a goat is having regular contractions at close intervals then stops completely a beginner should always get help quickly, preferably from a vet who will be able to instruct and advise. Never leave a goat in labour unattended for more than 20 or 30 minutes.

The placenta (afterbirth) should come away cleanly and completely within a few hours of the goat kidding. Once it has dropped, remove it to prevent the goat eating it; it could give her indigestion, and goats have choked to death while trying to eat the afterbirth. Sometimes the membranes are left hanging out which means that 'cleansing' has not been completed. Don't be tempted to pull them as this will cause a haemorrhage. It's never easy to decide just when to ask for veterinary advice; however, all things considered, it's probably best to err on the side of caution and seek expert advice early rather than late. Metritis or inflammation of the uterus could result from an incomplete cleansing, (see veterinary section, page 70).

Whilst waiting for the afterbirth to come away turn your attention to the kid(s) and mother. Give the goat a drink of warm water mixed with something sweet, glucose, molasses or brown sugar perhaps. I actually offer mine a choice of plain, sweet or salt water in three different bowls. The sooner the kid takes its first feed the better and if you can give it in a bottle you can see how much it has taken. Wipe the goat's udder with a warm damp cloth and then dry it. Make sure that you have ready a kid's feeding bottle that you have warmed in water. Squeeze some of the thick yellow colostrum or first milk into the bottle, pull the teat on and give the kid a feed; (don't be alarmed if the colostrum is not thick and yellow, it does vary). It's vital to ensure that all kids are given colostrum as it contains important antibodies, minerals and laxatives; it also helps to warm and comfort the kids. While the very first feed may be as little as 50mls, I always let them have as much as they want that first time. If a kid only takes a little you will need to come back to it very soon. Some latch onto the bottle easily, others need a bit of gentle persuasion. Take care that the hole in the teat is not too big or the kids could choke. Once they have fed they will sleep.

When the kids are settled, clean and tidy the goat's pen and put down fresh straw. Next draw off enough milk from the mother to relieve any tightness in the udder and refrigerate the milk for the kids' next feed. It's important never to milk a newly kidded goat dry for at least the first forty eight hours, particularly if she is a heavy milker; if you do you will run the risk of causing 'milk fever' resulting from the sudden loss of calcium (see page 71). The first milk is always very rich in this mineral.

Non dairy goats are usually left to suckle their kids.

Palatable plant - Ivy — NEVER berries or flowers.

Aftercare of the newly kidded goat

Offer the mother a little ivy (without the berries) cabbage or other fresh green food. Make sure the hay in her rack is the best and see if she would like some bran mash with soaked sugar beet pulp perhaps, then leave her to rest.

It's very important not to give your goat too much to eat in the way of concentrates for at least a week after kidding. Milk her little and often for the first few days to ease her udder; this could be as many as four times on the first day if she is a heavy milker. By the forth day you should have established a routine of twice daily milking. At this stage the milk will be free of colostrum and ready for the house. Here is a useful tip: if you have any extra colostrum freeze it, it could be a life saver if a goat should kid down without any milk at all.

After kidding discharge

It is quite usual for a freshly kidded goat to have a slight discharge for the first few days after kidding, and then, about a week later to start quite a heavy one. This can be very alarming for a novice but it's usually nothing to worry about. It should gradually lessen and clear up altogether in about three weeks. It's a good idea to wash the tail and surrounding area once a day until the discharge stops; if left it can make the goat very sore.

I always check the goat's temperature (102.5 F or 39 C) once a day after milking for the first week or so when she is discharging. If she is eating well and her temperature is normal there is nothing to worry about. If her temperature differs from the norm or there is any unpleasant smell, consult your vet at once.

Rearing new kids

In the dairy goat world, particularly amoungst the showing fraternity, most kids are bottle reared, whereas keepers of non-showing dairy goats often allow the kids to run with their dams and so help themselves. I still feel it's a good idea to give that very first feed from a bottle. This could be an advantage if the dam should become ill and die. There are many ways to rear kids and in the end you must choose the way which suits you best. Some dairy goat breeders give the first feed from the bottle and then see that the kids are suckling and leave them to run with their dams. They stay together for four days and the kids help themselves to the colostrum rich milk. They are then removed and bottle reared using the dams' milk. The reason for doing it this way is that you are in control of the goat's udder and the amount of milk each kid is taking. Also, if the very first feed was from a bottle, the kids should return to it without any trouble when they are taken from their mothers.

Once the kids are eating hard feed the bottles can be gradually phased out at four to six months depending on the breed. The one drawback I have found with this method is that it can be difficult if you want to run all your goats together. Goats generally make good mothers so many a kid will go back and help itself, remembering those first few days, while the dam will be only too pleased! However, I have found that if I rear kids entirely on the bottle they can all run together after four or five days and will not bother their mothers for milk as they have never suckled from them; they look to you and the bottle for nourishment while their mothers teach them about grazing. This is an easy system as you are in complete control: you know how much milk your goats are giving and how much your kids are taking. A kid which is being reared on its dam needs milk for at least the first four months of its life so unless you intend to sell the dam with the kid you are stuck with them both; this could be difficult to cope with for a beginner. A kid reared on the bottle can be sold as soon as it's ready providing the buyer has a supply of goat's milk. Never sell a kid until it is at least one month old.

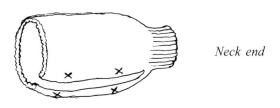

Neck end

Attach ties at X
Kid coat made from a jumper sleeve.

Bottle rearing kids, dairy type:

Birth to 1 week: 50mls increasing to 250mls 4 times per day.

1 week to 2 weeks: 400mls 4 times per day.

2 weeks to 8 weeks: 450mls to 500mls 4 times per day.

8 weeks to 10 weeks: 500mls 3 times per day.

10 weeks to 13 weeks: if eating well 500mls twice per day, otherwise continue 3 times per day.

13 weeks to 14 weeks: decrease to 500mls once per day.

Some very experienced breeders wean their kids from as early as 13 to 14 weeks as long as they are eating a good variety of foods by then. A lot will depend on the size of the kid and maybe the breed. Some say that early weaning leads to a better milker. Personally I have fed all my kids on the bottle until they were about 6 months old, and who is to say they would have milked any better had they been weaned earlier!

The Kids

Male Kids

Do not keep male kids as the demand for them is very limited. Never give male kids away as pets; they invariably end up as unwanted and sadly neglected animals, (see section on male goats, page 46).

Female kids

These should be carefully inspected. Make sure they are free from defects such as double teats (fish tail), extra teats (supernumerary) or a double orifice in a teat. Check also for face or jaw defects such as twisted, over- or under-shot mouths. Kids with unsound legs or other structural faults should be culled at birth. It can be hard to detect faults in very young animals, but it's a good idea to check your kids regularly as strange things can sometimes develop as they grow.

Don't be tempted to sell kids in an open market and always use a vet for any culling that has to be done. Rearing kids is a costly business and therefore it really doesn't pay to rear anything but the best. If, on reflection, these responsibilities seem too difficult to take on, then perhaps dairy goat keeping is not for you.

Disbudding of kids

Having examined your kids for faults or abnormalities you need to check them next for horn buds, particularly if they are a dairy breed. This applies to all breeds, but some non dairy goat keepers find horned goats acceptable to keep.

Hornless
or polled

Horned (if not disbudded by a vet
will develop horns

You may be able to feel two small pimples on top of your kid's head under two small whirls of hair (see diagram). These are horn buds which, if left, will grow into horns. It is inadvisable to allow a dairy goat to grow up with horns as they can do untold damage to both people and other goats. Any kid with horn buds at birth should be disbudded as soon as ready from between two and ten days old. This is a job for a vet.

Polled stock

A very important point which must not be overlooked when breeding is the question of horns. Goats with horns can be dangerous so almost all dairy goat kids born with hornbuds are disbudded by a vet when about a week old. Some goats are naturally hornless, or polled, but it's not a good idea to mate two polled animals with each other; there is a genetic factor which could result in the progeny being born hermaphrodite or infertile which would be difficult for the novice goat keeper to detect. So be wise and if your goat is naturally polled use a horned (disbudded) male or vice versa. It is rare for these problems to arise when breeding from two horned or disbudded animals.

45

Male goats

Keeping an entire male goat is an option not to be undertaken lightly. It is really best left to breeders and is not a job for the novice, the weak or the timid.

Male goats are generally affectionate animals; they like to rub their heads against most things and their attendants will certainly receive this treatment as well if the male goat is given half a chance. Male goats have a very powerful odour which is present at all times, and is even stronger during the breeding season! This smell will cling to your clothing, hands, watch strap, anything it comes into contact with, and it can be very difficult to remove. If the male is kept with the females everything takes on his aroma including the owner, other goats, the goathouse, your own home if you are not very careful, and especially the milk. This is one reason why the goat has a reputation for being a smelly animal which produces nasty-tasting milk; when female goats are correctly managed and give clean, hygienically produced milk, then nothing could be further removed from this undesirable scenario. It is all down to the male goat and his management or rather mis-management.

Do you really need to keep an entire male goat? If you have only a small number of females, 6 or fewer, or a good male of the right breed nearby (not too closely related to your stock) I would say 'no'. Remembering also that A.I. is readily available, why go to the expense of keeping a stud male goat for 365 days of the year, when his services are only required, if things go right, for one month of the year? For example: if a goat is mated on 1st November and does not need to return approximately 21 days later, then the male goat's services are no longer required.

Reasons for breeding

If you have decided to keep dairy goats, then the most obvious reason for breeding is to produce milk. Using the nearest available stud male is not necessarily the best option however. He will certainly get your goat in kid and she will milk but he may not be improving the quality of your future stock.

It's a good idea to spend some time looking at pedigrees if possible, and use the very best male of your chosen breed that you can find. A goat keeper who has no interest in showing might understandably question the need for this, but breeders will always select the best male goats from proven lines; these males carry in their genes the qualities of their dams which they in turn will pass on to their daughters. These offspring should be an improvement on their dams, many factors coming into the equation such as milk yield, length of lactation, quality of butter fat and protein content, and the general conformation of the goat along with the breed type.

Pedigree dairy goats registered with the B.G.S.

The B.G.S. has a comprehensive system of distinguishing signs and awards which pedigree dairy goats can carry in prefix and affix form beside their registered name and number. The signs and awards are related to the milking abilities of the goat.

Palatable plant - Ash. Take care
not to feed keys,

FEEDING

It's important to remember that goats are not dustbins and, as already mentioned, they would rather starve than eat rubbish.

All goats are browsers. They enjoy twigs and branches from hedges and trees as they require a constant supply of fibrous food to enable their digestive systems to function properly. Willow of all kinds is a particular favourite, in fact they will de-bark certain trees if given the chance. They will graze when the grass is good and enjoy vegetable trimmings and some clean household vegetable waste. They are also particularly keen on dried pea and bean haulm, but you must check that you are not feeding them anything poisonous such as potatoe haulm (tops) or rhubarb (see list of poisonous plants, page 61). The most important fibrous food is good quality hay which MUST be available at all times. Before you put it in the rack give it a sniff; it should smell fresh and sweet without any trace of mustiness. Hay that falls apart in the bale is often good. If it clings together the chances are it is not for goats; for every mouthful eaten many more will be rejected and dropped.

Goats will eat good quality clean oat, barley and pea straw but the feed

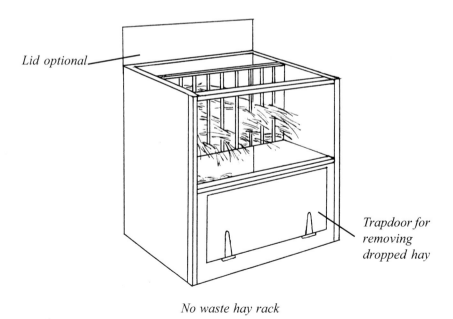

Lid optional

Trapdoor for removing dropped hay

No waste hay rack

value of these is not so high. Lucerne (alfalfa) and clover hay are excellent. They are legume hays and are often very expensive and difficult to find.

It's important that hay is stored correctly in a dry, airy building. Stack the bales on wooden pallets to keep them off the floor so the damp cannot rise up into them. Try to ensure that the building is vermin proof so there is no chance of the hay becoming soiled by rats or cats and dogs. Likewise any free range poultry must be kept out as your goats would certainly refuse to eat hay that has been contaminated by chicken droppings.

Both lucerne and grasses are available artificially dried. They are expensive but if you feed them carefully there will be very little waste. At least half the goat's diet (on a dry weight basis) should consist of forage, with concentrates (dry feeds), grains and seeds making up the balance. Store these in vermin proof containers. Dustbins are excellent but do remember to clean them out regularly.

A goat's total ration of concentrates should be given as not less than two feeds a day, although I divide it up into three feeds. Concentrates are as essential to the diet as forage. Cereal grains consist of whole or crushed oats, barley which comes whole, rolled or micronised (better for the digestion) and cooked or micronised flaked maize. These are often fed as a mixture with crushed peas, soya meal or linseed flakes to increase the protein content. Dried sugar beet pulp is sometimes added but more often fed seperately after being soaked in hot water for 4 to 6 hours. Variety in the diet is essential.

Ready mixed goat concentrates known as 'coarse mix' are available from agricultural corn merchants and are probably best used by the novice goat keeper to begin with.

Additional feeds

There are a number of additional feeds on the market, some designed exclusively for goats and others for horses but which can be useful for goats. As I have already mentioned, sugar beet pulp is popular with dairy goat breeders who often add bran to it. Other foods to add variety are field grass, Readigrass and other types of dried grasses, and lucerne nuts. Horsehage and other kinds of haylage are also enjoyed by most goats. Any change in their diet must be made gradually so that the digestive system can adjust.

Anglo Nubian Female

British Alpine Female

British Saanen Female

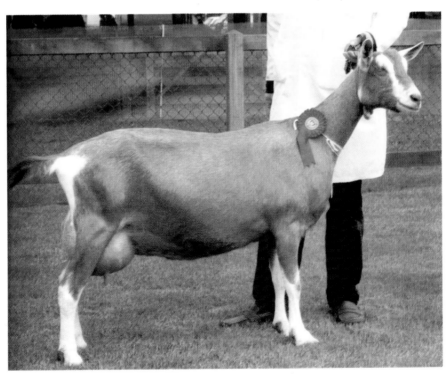

British Toggenburg Female

Pure Saanen Female

Pure Toggenburg Female

Golden Guernsey Goatling

Angora Buck

Boer Goat Female

Bagot Goat Male

Pygmy Goat Female

Herd Book (Any other variety) AOV female

Anglo Nubian Male

Pure Saanen Male

56

Anglo Nubian Male.

Left disbudded, right polled.

Minerals and vitamins

Goats need access to minerals and vitamins to supplement what they obtain in their food. Each goat pen should have an individual salt lick, preferably high in cobalt, and plain salt should be on offer as well. The salt lick comes in a brick sized block and you can buy a specially designed holder for it which can be fixed to the side of the goat's pen. Most ready made goat mixes have added minerals but these may be minerally inadequate.

My goats help themselves to their lick whenever they need it, and I keep an eye on which animal uses it and how often. Mineral content will vary throughout the U.K. so get advice from your vet or ask a local goatkeeper. This is a complex subject so it's best to have professional help.

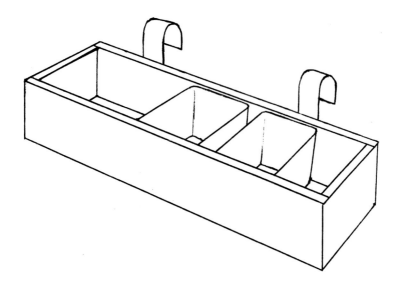

Mineral rack or food hanger
Home-made food hanger with removable plastic mineral or food containers.
Tip: do not overfill if using for minerals. Keep contents fresh and containers clean.
Brick sized mineral licks will fit into the containers.

Fresh clean water must be available at all times so refill the buckets twice a day even if they are not empty. Some goat keepers will give their animals a choice of three different waters: plain, salt or sweet (molasses or sugar). I offer my goats salt or sweet water in two separate bowls. It's less wasteful this way although it does take a little more time.

How much concentrate to feed?

This is a difficult question as the answer depends on a number of things.

First I would suggest that you check the weight capacity of the scoop you will be using; a scoop of oats will not weigh the same as one of bran for example.

Assuming your goat is in good condition, you can use the following as a guide. It comes by courtesy of the B.G.S. which has produced an excellent booklet on feeding goats. The author would advise any new goat keeper to buy a copy.

Dairy goats in milk:

A concentrate ration of 500gms for maintenance plus about 200gms for every litre of milk being produced each day.

Pregnant goats:

Concentrate rations need to be fed in the last 6 weeks of gestation starting with a small amount and increasing to about 1 to 1.5kgs for a large dairy goat, .5kg for a fibre or meat goat and 200 to 300gms for a pygmy goat.

Young stock:

200 to 600gms depending on size and time since weaning. You must keep an eye on the condition of your animals, especially goatlings who can easily get too fat if over fed.

These recommendations are for the quantities of a goat's daily rations which must be fed in addition to plenty of good quality forage.

SOME PALATABLE PLANTS AND TREES

Hogweed

Cowslip

Goose Grass (Cleavers)

Wild Chervil

Hedge Parsley

Lady's Slipper

Elm

Maple

Knapweed

Common Thistle

Red Dead Nettle

Silverweed

Groundsel

Red Campion

Wild Carrot

Ragged Robin

Hawthorn

Hazel

Dandelion

Sow Thistle

Chicory

Shepherds Purse

Heather or Ling

Tufted Vetch & Bush

Meadow Vetch

Wild Sanfoin

Willow Herb

Fat Hen

Common Nettle

Dock

Chickweed

Bladder Campion

Bindweed

Wild Thyme

Yarrow

Bramble (useful if goat is scouring)

Ash (take care not to feed keys)

Willow, all types (see medicinal section)

Common Red Clover & White, not so popular

Ivy (NEVER berries or flowers)

Holly (NEVER the berries)

Oak (NEVER use oak apples or acorns) A few oak leaves are fine and very good for a scouring goat.

SOME POISONOUS PLANTS AND TREES TO AVOID

Alder (causes scouring)

Yew (deadly)

Potatoe haulms

Aconite

Arum

Azalea

Anemone

Bracken

Nightshades (all)

Broom

Butterbur

Buttercup (in excess)

Box

Briony

Celandine

Charlock

Cupressus

Daffodil

Dog's Mercury

Pennycress

Foxglove

Fool's Parsley

Fungi

Ground Ivy

Gladiolus

Spindle (all parts)

Thorn Apple

Tansy

Buckthorn

Laburnum (all parts are deadly)

Tomato plants

Gourds

Hellebore

Holm Oak (see medicinal section)

Horsetail (Mare's Tail)

Iris

Juniper

Knotgrass

Knotweed

Lilac

Lupin

Marsh Mallow

Mugwort

Mulleins

Old Man's Beard

Poppy

Privet

Pine

Ragwort

Rhubarb

Rush

Spurge Laurel

Traveller's Joy

Tormentil

Rhododendron (lethal if not treated quickly)

COMMON DISEASES AND AILMENTS

Here is a list of what should be in your home goat First Aid box:

Your vet's telephone number (I have mine on auto-dial)
Thermometer, a digital rectal thermometer is ideal
Drenching bottle and/or large 50ml + syringe (always use a plastic bottle)
Bicarbonate of soda
Antiseptic e.g. Dettol
Antiseptic powder and spray (from vets or agricultural merchants)
Vegetable cooking oil (not corn oil)
Glucose powder, glycerine, treacle
Rehydration fluids (from vets or agricultural merchants)
Iodine and foot spray
Hydrogen Peroxide
Wormer and flea powder
Cotton wool
Scissors
Torch (in working order)
Medicines Record Book (always record treatments)
Goat coats large and small

First of all you must understand and be familiar with what a healthy goat is like.

Learn how to take a goat's temperature.

Restrain the animal then lubricate the end of your digital thermometer and insert it into the rectum. Remove it when you hear it bleep which tells you the temperature is reached. A goat's normal temperature is 39 C or 102.5 F. A sub-normal temperature is usually potentially more serious than a high one but both must be investigated.

Study the movement of the rumen.

This is on the left side of the goat's body above the flank if you are standing behind it looking up along its back. Place your hand gently but firmly on the goat's side and hold it there; you will be able to feel soft rumbling and churning movements, signs of a healthy animal. It is as well to familiarise yourself with how this feels as in almost all cases where a goat is sick the rumen stops working and the animal stops cudding.

Check the condition of the coat.

The coat should normally lie flat on the body and face and is usually thicker in winter. If it is fluffed up and on end, especially on the face, check the goat's temperature and rumen function. If both are normal you could treat the animal for a possible chill. Rug it up well, add more bedding and give a chill stimulant. If the rumen is not working and the temperature is abnormal consult your vet.

A healthy goat's dung should be in the form of round pellets.

Following is a list of common diseases and ailments.

Abortion

The novice should seek veterinary help and advice in this situation. If the goat was far enough into its pregnancy to have developed an udder, then start milking to encourage a milk yield; make sure you do it little and often to begin with.

Abscesses

These should never be neglected. Don't ever be tempted to lance them yourself; instead treat with hot fomentations. Abscesses can develop for various reasons. If they are situated on the head along the jaw line it could be the result of a bad tooth or wounds from fighting, or even eating thorns. If they occur on the body they could be at the site of past injections. Consult your vet. (See section on CL, top of page 33).

The Kids' first outing

Goats yarded

Goats grazing, Golden Guernseys

Anglo Nubians

Goats at home

Goat Show

66

Showing dairy goats - Inter Breed Championship

Top of the line

Acetonaemia (ketosis)

This is a condition which can result from incorrect feeding. It is usually contracted by dairy goats soon after kidding but can also occur just before (see Pregnancy Toxaemia, page 71). The animal's whole system becomes unbalanced. The symptoms to look out for are the goat going off her concentrate feed, prefering hay, her milk yield falling, and a sweet smell of acid drops on her breath or coming from her bedding, or both.

First aid treatment for acetonemia: give the goat 100mls of glycerine in warm water or you can use a heaped tablespoon of glucose powder, treacle or brown sugar; different goats have different preferences; seek your vet's advice on this. Remember, a lactating goat requires an enormous amount of high energy foods. Take care not to overdo the protein just before kidding and particularly afterwards for a few weeks. A high energy drench such as propylene glycol (obtainable from your vet or agricultural merchant) is given by mouth and is essential although goats generally hate this treatment. Multi vitamin injections may also be of value. A Glucose and High Energy block can be very useful. It might be helpful to have these available ad lib for 2 to 3 months before and after kidding. When it comes to acetonemia prevention is definitely better than cure.

Bloat - chronic indigestion (colic)

This is technically not an illness but a condition that can kill. It is typically caused by eating too much wet, frosted or lush grass. Over eating, often concentrates, and travelling, can also cause rapid build-ups of gas in the rumen (first of the four stomachs) and you may find the left flank particularly becoming swollen and tight. Cudding stops and you will not be able to feel the rumen moving. The goat can look very distressed, standing with her head down, her coat on end and her face hair all fuzzy.

First Aid treatment for bloat, milkers (less for young stock): mix 50mls of cooking oil (not corn oil) with a heaped teaspoon of bicarbonate of soda. Shake it well then drench the goat with the mixture. (Be warned, they don't generally like this!) Massage the swollen stomach vigorously and try to encourage the animal to move about. If there is no sign of rumen movement repeat the exercise in 10 minutes. If after half an hour there is still no sign of improvement get veterinary help quickly.

Cloudburst (False Pregnancy)

This condition sometimes occurs in goats that are not mated each year, and can cause problems in goatlings where breeding has been delayed. After mating, or occasionally without being mated, the goat's body increases in size and she appears to be in kid. Suddenly, and often when the goat would be due to kid had it been mated, a mass of yellow watery fluid floods out as if a water bladder had burst; of course there is no kid. Sometimes all you find is a goat with a wet rear end and a soaking wet pen.

Take the goat for remating on her first heat after the discharge has completely cleared up, if you intend to breed from her.

Coccidiosis

This can affect goats of all ages.It is caused by a protozoan parasite called coccidia. There are various symptoms including a watery scour with mucus and a little blood. If you see this then it is quite likely to be caused by coccidiosis. (However, in my early days of goat keeping I lost a very young kid to coccidiosis and there was no scouring, the kid just rejected its bottle.) Vets will diagnose the problem from a dung sample and then provide treatment. With all types of scour goats will benefit from a course of rehydration fluids; these are available either as a liquid or as a powder to which you add water.

Digestive scour

Cut out concentrates and give plenty of hay and a good double handful of oak leaves, (use dried ones in winter). Bramble leaves can also help settle things down. If the scouring continues check your worming programme. No matter how careful your management, you should always worm your goats regularly. Try to vary your worming medication by using a different one each year. Get advice on this from your vet.

Palatable plant -
Bramble, useful if goat
is scouring.

Discharges

From the nose: goats do catch colds and providing the animal is bright and eating well there is no need to worry. Always check temperatures, twice daily with kids. Anything different from normal could indicate a problem which would need to be dealt with by a vet.

From the eyes: always seek veterinary advice if there is any discharge from the eyes.

From the rectum, scour (diarrhoea): there are various problems which can cause this. With kids it could be as simple as a dirty bottle, so always wash teats and bottles very thoroughly, and give the next feed as plain water.

Lice and mites

These are treated with Louse Powder or Pour-ons which you sprinkle over the goat's body, avoiding the head.

Mastitis

There are several types of this disease which affect the udder.

Acute: the udder becomes swollen, very inflamed and hard; the milk has clots rather like the broken up skin on top of boiled milk and there may be some blood present. The goat's temperature is often very high.

Sub-acute: this is harder to detect but clots can also appear. In all suspected cases veterinary assistance will be needed.

Metritis

This is an infection of the uterus which can follow a difficult or assisted kidding. A thick strawberry coloured discharge is produced which has a most unpleasant smell, and the goat will run a high temperature and refuse to eat. It's obviously far better to prevent this happening in the first place, so it's advisable to check a newly kidded goat's temperature a number of times if she has had a difficult or assisted kidding. Treatment will be a course of antibiotic injections from your vet.

Milk Fever

This condition can occur shortly after kidding and can be very dramatic. The goat will probably collapse, her neck will twist backwards and she may also have convulsions; cudding will stop. It is caused by too much milk being produced too quickly and depleting the whole system of calcium. Too much high protein food in the goat's diet immediately before and after kidding can also help to cause milk fever. Treatment is usually with calcium borogluconate administered by injection under the skin. A novice should always seek veterinary assistance with this very quickly.

Pregnancy Toxaemia (Twin Lamb/Kid Disease)

In late pregnancy the extra demands made upon the goat's body become very high, even more so if she is carrying more than one kid which most goats do. General symptoms are that she stops cudding, is off her food and is reluctant to move; she may even go blind. First Aid treatment: drench the goat with glucose or molasses mixed with warm water and seek professional help at once. The food given before and after kidding must provide large amounts of energy (see section on feeding).

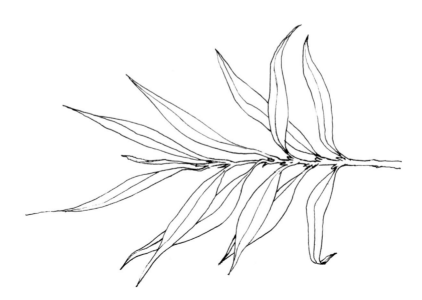

Palatable plant - Crack Willow

Treatments and their administration

Injecting

This should be taught by a vet or an experienced goat keeper.

Oral remedies

Drenching, giving liquid medicine by mouth. Back your goat into a corner then put one hand under its chin and tilt the head slightly upwards. Hold the mixture in its container with the other hand; if you use a large syringe you will find you have more control than if you use a plastic bottle. Insert the syringe or bottle into the corner of the goat's mouth and remember to always administer the medicine very slowly in a trickle. Make sure she is swallowing by watching her throat. If she coughs stop drenching immediately and wait for her to regain her breath before continuing. Some animals are easier to drench than others. You may need a second person to help restrain some animals.

There are oral remedies which some goats will drink from a bowl and kids will take in their bottles.

Pour-ons or injections

These are liquids which kill both internal and external parasites but not coccidiosis. Ask your vet's advice before you buy and use these.

Note

When using any type of medication on your goats it's very important to check the withdrawal times if you are using the milk for human consumption. Remember to keep a record of treatments given.

DAIRYING

The all important word here is HYGIENE.

EQUIPMENT

Milking bucket: this should be stainless steel; a gallon widebase with a lid would be ideal; plastic is not advisable.

Strainer: the milk is poured through this into the collecting vessel. There are stainless steel strainers with filters on the market, but they can be very expensive. A sieve which is large enough to take a milk filter will do; it should work adequately as long as the milk is poured through carefully.

Churn: to hold the milk.

Milk filters

Udder wipes: for cleaning the udder prior to milking.

Teat dip and cup: the teats are dipped into the mixture in the cup after milking to help prevent any bacteria entering the udder via the teat orifice.

Washing-up equipment: a brush, dairy detergent and steriliser.

The Milking Area

This needs to be easy to wash down and keep clean. Wooden milk benches are good but if you buy one I would recommend using a rubber mat on its floor; this provides a non-slip surface for the goat to stand on and it's easy to remove for cleaning.

Always milk the goat outside her pen in a place where you can tie her up securely.

Milking

This is not difficult to master but to begin with it will make your hands ache a little; persevere and you will be fine. There is no right or wrong side to milk from.

Gather your milking equipment together then secure the goat's head and sit down close to her side. Wipe the udder to clean it and remove any loose hair etc. Never pull down on the teats while milking; when the author was taught she was told that she should be able to keep a coin balanced on the base of her thumb where it joined her hand. Place the bucket under the goat then put your hands gently round the teats which should lie against your fingers. Now put your thumbs across the front of the teats and compress them with your thumbs against your top fingers to cut off the milk supply from the udder. Squeeze out the milk in the teat by closing your fingers one after the other to empty it; relax your thumbs and more milk will flow into the teat. Do one teat then the other alternately until the udder appears empty, then gently rub both hands round the udder from the top where it joins the goat's body, down to the teats; you will find this brings down more milk. Do this several times to extract all the milk. This is called 'stripping out', and it is this last milk which contains most of the butterfat. When the udder is empty move the bucket to one side and apply the teat dip. Put the milk in a safe place and return the goat to her pen.

The milk should be cooled as soon as possible so strain it through the filter and refrigerate it. Rinse all the milking equipment in cold water first then wash it in hot water using a detergent. Next rinse it out with a steriliser and finish with a final rinse in clean water.

Try to keep to regular milking times. You are aiming to milk out your goats as quickly, quietly, gently and thoroughly as possible.

If you intend to sell any surplus milk you will need to be licensed and approved by your local Health Authority.

MILK PRODUCTS

Cream

Goat's cream is white and very delicious. It can be obtained by separating or clotting the milk.

Butter

This is made from the cream and can be produced by using an electric mixer. Remember it will be white but you can add colouring which is obtainable from dairy suppliers.

Yogurt

This is easy to make. You will need some starter (also available from dairy suppliers) or live yogurt. The higher the butterfat content of the milk, the better the consistency of the yogurt.

Cheese

Cheese rennet is available from dairy suppliers and soft and hard varieties of cheese are easy to make.

Goat milk freezes well and will thaw correctly overnight in the fridge.

For detailed information on making these various milk products, the author would recommend a visit to your local library which should have appropriate books on the subject.

Some breeders in B.G.S. approved clubs milk record their goats. The yield is recorded by weight in kilos, and butterfat and protein samples are taken monthly. The results are accumulated and at the end of the lactation any milk figures gained are recognised by the B.G.S. and added to the goat's pedigree.

SHOWING

Showing is the breeder's shop window and many County Shows have classes for most breeds of goat.

Dairy Goats

The B.G.S. publishes details of shows that they recognise. Some shows are organised by Goat Clubs and nearly all County and Club goat events are supported by the B.G.S., including male shows which have youngstock as well. These however, tend to be one day affairs, while County Shows and, to a certain extent, Club shows which hold 24 hour milking trials, always require at least one overnight stay.

If you are entering milking goats you will need to be present the day before the show starts as all goats entered for milking have to be milked out at a specified time and stripped out by the stewards. All the competing goats will then be starting out on an equal footing and will be milked at specified times in the morning and afternoon. The milk is weighed and recorded; butterfat and protein samples are taken and sent to a laboratory for analysis. Milking goats that are also entered in inspection classes are judged very early in the morning with full udders. They are then milked as described above and later judged again. This time the judge will have details of all the morning yields along with the dates of kidding and the ages of the goats; their conformation and breed types will also be taken into consideration. A dairy goat judge has to be familiar with all the different breed standards as there is only one judge for the whole dairy goat section. Awards given by the B.G.S. will only be verified when the final calculations are made and analyst reports completed. Show class places remain as given but the B.G.S. awards may not hold; so off to another show to try again!

When it comes to showing youngstock, the author always considers this to be a basic training for the more serious side of showing goats and taking part in milking trials.

Angoras

These are shown for type, fleece and conformation while their all important and very valuable shorn fleeces are judged separately.

All other breeds are judged on breed type and conformation.

Palatable plant - Ivy, NEVER berries or flowers.

FOOT TRIMMING

This job will need to be done approximately every 4 to 6 weeks and it would be a good idea to ask an experienced goat keeper to show you how to do it.

You will need a pair of hoof shears, and a small surform rasp would also be helpful. Secure the goat's head then pick up the first foot in the same manner as for shoeing a horse. (Goats are NOT upended as sheep are when their feet are trimmed.) Hold the hoof firmly in one hand and clean away any debris with the other; then cut off any overgrown horn from either side of the hoof and trim the heel down to the same level as the sole. Do take care at the tip (toe) because the blood vessels are very near to the surface at this point and it's all too easy to draw blood. Foot trimming does take practice; trim off a little at a time till you achieve a clean flat surface then you can finish off with the surform.

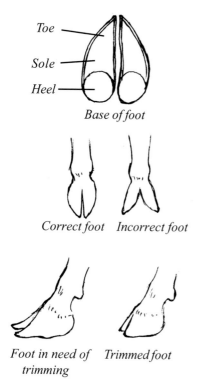

Toe

Sole

Heel

Base of foot

Correct foot   *Incorrect foot*

Foot in need of trimming   *Trimmed foot*

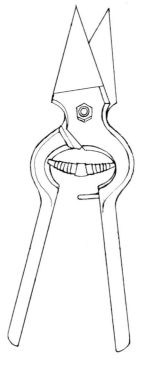

Foot clippers

78

KEEPING RECORDS

There are two compulsory records you must keep if you have livestock, and this includes goats.

Movement Records

You are required by Law to keep records of all movements; this involves a written record book and also DEFRA's movement papers. You will need an exercise book with columns and headings for the information. This book is a legal document and must show the date of movement, the addresses of where the goat came from and where it is going, the sex of the animal and the goat identification, that is the herd mark and the individual animal number which is either a tattoo or on a tag.

DEFRA will supply you with a pad of movement forms; you retain one and the others travel with the goat. On arrival at the destination, one copy of the forms will be sent to DEFRA, the haulier and purchaser will keep the others.

Medicine Book

This is also a legal document and again, an exercise book will be suitable. The information you need to keep in it will be the names and batch numbers of all medicines administered to your goats with the relevant ear tag or tattoo numbers of the goat and the date you gave the treatments together with amounts given. Always note milk withdrawal times if any.

Animal Identification

Any goat born on or after 1st July 2005 must carry its identification details on an ear tag: these will consist of the herd mark starting with U.K. on one side and the individual animal number on the reverse. Some goats born before the above date already carry tags while others, if registered with the B.G.S. or a Breed Society, have ear tattoos. Herd/flock numbers must be obtained from DEFRA.

I would also recommend keeping a third book, a personal diary. In it you can record dates of matings and expected kiddings, foot trimming, vets' visits and the reasons they called and anything else which is relevant to your goat keeping management.

Legal requirment at the time of going to press:

The Law states that any goat aged over 18 months which dies on your farm or during transport must be reported to DEFRA. This applies to all goats that die naturally and to those that are killed on your farm other than for human consumption.

To report these animals phone DEFRA, 7 days a week free-phone, on 0800 525890.

Palatable plant - Holly

QUESTIONS MOST ASKED
BY GOAT KEEPERS

Q) Why won't my goat eat her corn feed?

A) Is she cudding? If the answer is yes there is not too much to worry about. Stand back and observe her; if she is behaving normally wash out her food container and try to tempt her with some natural things like ivy leaves or willow, docks or slightly wilted nettles. Offer her some apple or chopped roots, swede, carrots or potatoes (but not green ones) or try her with banana skins which some goats love. Don't overdo the corn ration but offer it little and often.

If the goat is not cudding check her for bloat and treat as necessary.

If she is pregnant or newly kidded check for Pregnancy Toxaemia or Acetonaemia. Are you overdoing the protein? Think energy foods (see section on feeding) especially at pre- and post-kidding times. Mix a tablespoon each of dried yeast powder (available from Health Food Shops - not the type used for bread making) and glucose into a pint of warm water and give this daily from about 2 weeks before the kidding date until 4 to 6 weeks afterwards

First Aid for a milker: tempt her with 1 tablespoon of glucose in a pint of warm water, or molasses. Your vet will supply you with a high energy drench if first aid fails. Goats heavy in kid do sometimes go off their corn feed.

Q) Why won't my goat eat her hay?

A) Maybe it's not good enough! Empty and clean out the rack then refill it lightly from a new bale.

Q) Why is my goat scouring?

A) Has she eaten too much of something? If she is bright and acting normally offer her just hay and a few oak leaves. Does she need worming? Check to see when you last did this. Could it be Coccidiosis? (see page 69) If the affected animal is a kid perhaps it has picked up an infection from a dirty feeding bottle or teat; these must always be kept scrupulously clean. As well as a bottle brush, a good tip is to keep an old toothbrush: they are excellent for cleaning the inside of screw-on tops to kids' bottles.

Q) Why has my goat got swollen crusty feet that she keeps biting?

A) This is very common and usually occurs in the winter. The cause is most likely to be a mite and some goats are more susceptible to it than others, it seems to run in families. Treat it with a pour-on for external parasites.

First Aid treatment: buy some Benzyl Benzoate from a chemist and rub it on the affected areas every other day for 3 or 4 days. The secret is to catch it early.

Palatable plant - Maple

QUESTIONS MOST ASKED BY NON-GOAT KEEPERS

Q) Which goat is best for milk?

A) There are good and bad in all breeds. Choose the breed which most pleases your eye. If you do your very best for your goat she will do her best for you.

Q) The grass is very long in my orchard so shall I buy a goat?

A) NO. Get some geese or sheep.

Q) What are those things hanging from the necks of some goats?

A) They are called "tassels" or "toggles"; nobody really knows their origin. Anglo-Nubian and Golden Guernsey goats should never have them but other dairy breeds can.

Once you have experienced goat keeping you will understand the following: Silly Billy, Get My Goat, Who's Kidding, and you'll realise how very wrong people are when they think that goats eat anything!

USEFUL ADDRESSES

The British Goat Society
Secretary: Ms S. Knowles, 34-36 Fore Street, Bovey Tracey, Newton Abbot, Devon, TQ13 9AD
Tel: 01626 833168 Fax: 01626 834536
E-mail: secretary@allgoats.com
Websites: www.allgoats.com and www.allgoats.org.uk

Allen & Page Smallholder Feeds
Norfolk Mill, Shipdham, Thetford, IP25 7SD
Tel: 01362 822900 Fax: 01362 822910
Website: www.smallholderfeed.co.uk

Ascott Smallholding Supplies Ltd.
The Old Creamery, Four Crosses, Llanymynech, Powys, SY22 6LP
Tel: 0845 1306285 Fax: 0870 7740140 Website: www.ascott.biz

Peter Collin (goat hayrack etc.)
French Hall Bungalow, Moulton, Newmarket, Suffolk, CB8 8RZ
Tel & Fax: 01638 750665 E-mail: peter@frenchall-goats.co.uk Website: http://www.frenchall-goats.co.uk

Acting the Goat

Index

87